THE DEATH OR GLORY BOYS

QUIZ BOOK

LEICESTER FOOTBALL CLUB

THE DEATH OR GLORY BOYS

QUIZ BOOK

LEICESTER
FOOTBALL CLUB

NIGEL FREESTONE

This edition published in Great Britain in 2013 by DB Publishing, an imprint of JMD Media.

Copyright © Nigel Freestone 2013

ISBN 9781780913322

Contents

LEICESTER TIGERS FOOTBALL CLUB

Calling all Leicester Tigers fans. How much do you know about the best-supported and most successful club in English rugby? From domination of the Midlands Cup in their formative years to national knockout cup conquests and to the top of the professional game, English and European titles, Leicester are the club every other wants to emulate. Well, now you can test your knowledge of your favourite rugby team with the 750 challenging questions in the Leicester Tigers Quiz Book. This quiz book tests your knowledge of the truly remarkable history of the Leicester Tigers from the 'Death or Glory Boys' to the Champions of Europe. The book aims to entertain and educate, and will score a hit with anyone who has a keen interest in the oval ball.

Chapter 1 – In the Beginning...

1. In what year was Leicester Football Club founded?

2. Leicester Football Club was formed at a meeting held in which Leicester Hotel?

3. Leicester Football Club was formed from the amalgamation of which three clubs?

4. Leicester Tigers are well known for their famous scarlet, green and white colours. But they didn't start with this strip. What colour strip did they start with?

5. Leicester Football Club played their first game in October 1880. Who were their first opponents?

6. Leicester's first game was played at home. Which ground staged the game – Spinney Hill Park, Belgrave Cricket and Cycle Ground or Mill Lane?

7. Leicester Football Club's first game finished nil-nil. True or False?

8. How much did it cost to watch Leicester Football Club play in their first season – 2d, 6d or 9d?

9. Leicester Football Club's first XV played 17 games in their first season. How many did they lose – 0, 1 or 3?

10. During the early 1880s Leicester Football Club also fielded a side playing association football. True or False?

11. Leicester played Northampton for the first time in November 1880. Who won the first 'East Midland derby'?

12. What was the first ever trophy won by the Tigers – Leicestershire Cup, Midlands Counties Cup or Leicestershire Charity Cup?

13. Can you name the first Leicester captain to win a trophy?

14. Leicester Football Club played home games at which public park in 1881 – Victoria Park, Abbey Park or Western Park?

15. Leicester Tigers reached their first ever final in 1889. Which club beat them 0–8 to win the Midland Counties Cup?

16. In what year did the Leicester Tigers wear their famous scarlet, green and white colours for the first time in a vertical stripe formation – 1881, 1888 or 1891?

17. Leicester moved to Welford Road in what year – 1888, 1892 or 1896?

18. Leicester Tigers first game at their current home ground Welford Road was a 17–0 victory against which club – Stoneygate Rugby Club, Old Newtonians or Leicestershire Rugby Union?

19. Welford Road had no clubhouse in the beginning. At which hotel did the players change and trot across the road to the ground?

20. Can you name Leicester's first opponents from London, who in 1892 thumped them 37–0 in the capital city?

21. Can you name the Leicester centre of the early 1890s, a favourite of the crowd who had the nickname 'clasher'?

22. What was the attendance at Welford Road for the Midland Counties Cup tie against Coventry in 1893 – 1,000, 10,000 or 15,000?

23. Between 1897 and 1905, Leicester dominated the premier league competition for Midland based clubs, the Midland Counties Cup. They then dropped out of the competition. What was the reason for their absence?

24. The Tigers beat Burfield Rangers, holders of the Leicestershire Senior Cup in 1894 by what score, at the time a club record – 51–0, 71–0 or 81–0?

25. Kick-off times during the 1890s tended to fluctuate depending on the arrival of trains carrying the away team and their supporters. True or False?

26. Leicester Football Club at the beginning of the twentieth century looked after the welfare of their players through an insurance policy against injury. How much was an injured player paid a week – 10 shillings, 15 shillings or 20 shillings?

27. Who became Leicester's club secretary on 2 August 1895, at the age 27?

28. Can you name the hooker who made his Leicester debut early in 1896, who in the next 14 years made 491 appearances for the Tigers?

29. Which grammar school did the Tigers play regularly in the late 1890s – Uppingham, Bedford or Oakham?

30. Which brilliant all-round sportsman who captained England in two cricket Test matches, made his Leicester debut against Bedford in April 1895?

Chapter 2 – Older or Younger?

Were the following clubs founded before or after Leicester Football Club? In other words are they Younger or Older?

31.   Northampton Saints. Younger or Older?

32.   Bath. Younger or Older?

33.   Nottingham. Younger or Older?

34.   Bristol. Younger or Older?

35.   Harlequins. Younger or Older?

36.   London Welsh. Younger or Older?

37.   Sale Sharks. Younger or Older?

38.   Exeter Chiefs. Younger or Older?

39.   Gloucester. Younger or Older?

40.   Gosforth. Younger or Older?

Chapter 3 – R.F.U. Club Competition

41. In what year did the first RFU Club Competition begin?

42. Who were the augural winners of the RFU Club Competition?

43. Which club has won the English Cup the most times?

44. Leicester Tigers first reached the John Player Cup Final in 1978. They were beat 6–3 by which team?

45. In 1979 Leicester beat Moseley by what score to win the John Player Cup for the first time – 9–6, 10–9 or 15–12?

46. Leicester Tigers won the John Player Cup three consecutive times between 1979 and 1981. Can you name the clubs they beat in the 1980 and 1981 John Player Cup Finals?

47. How many times have Bath beaten the Tigers in the Final of the RFU Club Competition?

48. Who succeeded John Player as sponsors of the Cup competition in 1979?

49. Gloucester and Moseley shared the John Player Cup in 1982 after a 12–12 draw in the final after extra time. True or False?

50. Who won the Cup six times from 1989 to 1996?

Chapter 4 – Edwardian Tigers

51.   Leicester in 1901 became the first club in three seasons to win at which ground?

52.   In what year did Welford Road host its first international when England beat Ireland 6–3 – 1899, 1902 or 1904?

53.   Approximately how many spectators crammed into Welford Road to watch England beat Ireland – 4,000, 10,000 or 14,000?

54.   Who became the first home-produced international for the club in 1903?

55.   Leicester met their first touring team in 1904, losing 28–0. Who were Leicester's opponents?

56.   The 1904 game with the tourists attracted 16,000 spectators with gate receipts of £392. What percentage of the gate was paid to the opposition – 10%, 70% or 90%?

57.   The Tigers game against Cambridge United was cancelled in 1904 because the University refused to play due to the conditions; the referee was so disgusted he joined the Tigers practice session. True or False?

58.   Who won five winners' medals consecutively in the Midland Counties Cup with the Tigers, scoring a hat-trick of tries in the 1905 Final?

59. According to a newspaper report Leicester "had too many of the men... showed the white feather and absolutely refused to go down on the ball to stop the rushes of the opposition' in a 27–6 defeat against which University in 1907?

60. The RFU in 1908 had a motion that Leicester should be expelled from the Union for what offence?

61. Can you name the three players who in 1907–8 became the first Tigers to play abroad when they toured Australia with the Anglo-Welsh party (a forerunner of the British Lions)?

62. Who made his debut for the Tigers in 1908 as a prop forward and held a place in the side until the outbreak of World War I?

63. Until the start of the professional era, there was an annual Boxing Day fixture against the Barbarians. In which year did this fixture begin – 1905, 1909 or 1919?

64. The first game between Leicester and the Barbarians ended in a 0–0 draw. True or False?

65. Who became the first Tigers player to be sent off, when he was given his marching orders by referee H.A. Taylor in game against the Harlequins in 1912?

66. Which team did the Tigers beat 65–0 in March 1912 – Stratford-upon-Avon, Newcastle-upon-Avon or Newbold-upon-Avon?

67. In 1914 two clubs from the same town contested the Midlands Cup Final. Who did Leicester beat in the Final to win the competition for the twelfth time in 16 years – Belgrave Premier Works, Aylestone Gas Works or Stoneygate RFU?

68. Who scored his 154th Tigers try in 1918 to become the club's leading try scorer?

69. Two Leicester games were played during the First World War to aid local recruitment to the armed forces and to raise funds for charity. Who were Leicester's opponents for both games?

70. According to a local sports journalist, "More ladies attend Leicester matches than is the case in any other centre – either rugby or association – in the United Kingdom. The presence of ladies tends to maintain a high tone...". True or False?

Chapter 5 – Heineken Cup

71. In what year was the inaugural Heineken Cup competition held?

72. Why is the Heineken Cup known as the H Cup in France?

73. Can you name the six countries whose club, regional and provincial teams contest the Heineken Cup?

74. How many teams contest the pool section of the Heineken Cup competition?

75. Who were the first winners of the Heineken Cup in 1995–96?

76. Teams that do not qualify for the Heineken Cup enter which second tier European rugby competition?

77. Who were the first club to win the Heineken Cup three times?

78. Can you name the first English club to win the Heineken Cup?

79. Who were the first team to win back-to-back Heineken Cups?

80. Can you name the first Welsh club to reach the final of the Heineken Cup?

Chapter 6 – 1997 Heineken Cup Final

81.   How many teams competed for the Heineken Cup in 1996–97?

82.   How many games did the Tigers lose in the pool stage of the 1996–97 Heineken Cup?

83.   Who did the Tigers beat 37–11 at Welford Road in front of 16,200 fans to reach the Heineken Cup Final for the first time in 1997?

84.   Which ground staged the 1997 Heineken Cup Final?

85.   Tigers played Brive in the 1997 Heineken Cup Final. In which country are Brive based?

86.   What was the half-time score?

87.   Who scored three penalties for the Tigers in the 1997 Heineken Cup Final?

88.   Were the Tigers ever in front during the 1997 Heineken Cup Final?

89.   Brive wing Sebastian Carrat scored two tries in his team's 28–9 win over Leicester Tigers in the 1997 Final. Carrat went on to represent France at which athletics event?

90.   Who scored one conversion, one drop goal and a penalty in the 1997 Heineken Cup Final?

Chapter 7 – Captain Fantastic

91. Can you name the Tigers captain in 1970–71 who became the club's honorary secretary in 1982?

92. Name the back row forward who captained the Tigers both before the Second World War and immediately afterwards.

93. Can you name Leicester Fosse's star striker who was appointed captain of Leicester Football Club between 1891–93?

94. Can you name the flanker who captained Leicester in 1968–69 and 1972–73?

95. Who captained Leicester in their three successive John Player Cup winning Finals between 1979–81?

96. Who captained Leicester from 1983–85 and played in five John Player Cup Finals?

97. Which Tigers' centre was appointed captain of England in 1985 for the Five Nations Championship and the summer tour to New Zealand?

98. Who in 1933–34 became the first Tiger to captain England?

99. Which back-row forward who played 239 games for the Tigers captained the British Lions teams to New Zealand and Australia in 1930?

100. Can you name the talented fly-half, capped for Scotland and Leicestershire county champion golfer who captained the Tigers between 1930 and 1932?

101. Who was the first captain to bring the Midland Counties Cup home to Leicester in 1898?

102. Who was Leicester's captain when they won the inaugural Courage Clubs Championship in 1988?

103. Which Tigers lock of the 1960s for many years enjoyed the distinction of being the only uncapped Englishman to have captained the Barbarians twice (against Penarth in 1967 and Swansea in 1968)?

104. Which Tigers captain won the Military Cross?

105. Who captained the Barbarians against England at Twickenham on the 30 May 2009, to a 33–26 victory?

106. How many times did Neil Back captain England?

107. Who was named as England captain for the 2005 Six Nations match against Italy and Scotland, in the absence of Jason Robinson?

108. Which England goal-kicking wing captained an all-Tigers Leicestershire side that won the county championship in 1925?

109. Who captained the Tigers to their tenth English title in 2013?

110. Which lock twice capped twice by England was Leicester's captain for the 1976–77 season?

Chapter 8 – 1920s Tigers

111. Can you name the goal kicking Tiger who on his international debut in 1920 scored and converted England's only try of the game?

112. The Welford Stand, later named the Crumbie Stand, was opened in October 1920 by the President of the Rugby Union. Can you name him?

113. Who scored 59 tries for the Tigers in 1919–20?

114. At Christmas 1921 Leicester Tigers entertained their first French visitors. Who were they?

115. Which country did the Tigers visit on their first foreign tour in 1922?

116. Who set a club record by scoring seven tries in the 36–0 hammering of Manchester at Welford Road in December 1922?

117. On 10 February 1923 England beat Ireland 23–5 at Welford Road in the last England home international played away from Twickenham until 1992. True or False?

118. Who took over the captaincy of the Tigers from George Ward in October 1923?

119. An estimated 35,000 packed Welford Road to the rafters to watch which 'invincible' tourists in 1924?

120. How much profit did the Tigers make from the 1924 tourist game – £10, £100 or £1,000?

121. Tom Crumbie would not allow Tigers players to turn out for the Barbarians. True of False?

122. Who captained the all-Tigers Leicestershire side that won the County Championship in 1925?

123. What unusual lunar event took place during the Tigers game against the Army in 1925?

124. Can you name the Leicester legend, scorer of 206 tries for the Tigers who played his final game in 1924?

125. Leicester forwards regularly began to wear letters as a means of identification against Bath at Welford Road in what year? 1919, 1926 or 1932?

126. Can you name *Leicester Mercury's* rugby correspondent in the 1920s who reported under the pseudonym 'Cyrus'?

127. Who in March 1927 became the first Tiger to score 1,000 career points during a home game to Old Merchant Tailors?

128. Which Welsh club had two players sent off in 8–5 defeat against the Tigers in 1928 at Welford Road – Cardiff, Newport or Swansea?

129. Who succeeded Tom Crumbie as the Tigers' Honorary Secretary in 1928?

130. On 29 January 1928 which team failed to turn up for a fixture, the first time this had happened since the Tigers started 'taking dates'?

Chapter 9 – Premiership Tigers Records

131. Who has made the most appearances for the Tigers in the Premiership?

132. Can you name the Tigers top points scorer in the Premiership?

133. Neil Back is Leicester's leading try scorer in the Premiership with how many tries – 29, 59 or 69?

134. Leicester's biggest victory in the Premiership, a 83–10 win in 2005, was against which club?

135. What is the highest number of points the Tigers have conceded in a Premiership fixture – 45, 55 or 65?

136. What is the most consecutive victories the Tigers have notched up in the Premiership – 11, 17 or 19?

137. Leicester Tigers have never lost more than three consecutive games in the Premiership. True or False?

138. Can you name Leicester's oldest point scorer in the Premiership?

139. What is the highest number of tries scored in a Premiership game involving Leicester Tigers – 9, 12 or 15?

140. Which holds the record for the scorer of the most hat-tricks for the Tigers in the Premiership (3)?

Chapter 10 – 2001 Heineken Cup Final

141. How many pool matches did the Tigers lose in the 2000–01 Heineken Cup competition?

142. Which French team did the Tigers beat in the pool stage of the 2001 Heineken Cup competition?

143. The Tigers were seeded number two at the end of the pool stage and faced Swansea in the quarter-finals of the 2000–01 Heineken Cup at Welford Road. What was the final score?

144. Which English club did the Tigers beat in the semi-finals to reach the 2001 Heineken Cup Final?

145. Which football ground staged Leicester's Heineken Cup semi-final in 2001?

146. The Tigers beat which French side to win the Heineken Cup for the first time in 2001?

147. Who was Leicester's captain in the 2001 Heineken Cup Final?

148. Can you name Leicester's Australian inside-centre in the 2001 Heineken Cup Final who was appointed the Tigers coach in 2005?

149. What was the attendance at the 2001 Heineken Cup Final – 24,000, 44,000 or 84,000?

150. Who scored five (5) penalties for the Tigers in the 2001 Heineken Cup Final?

151. Leicester brought on which replacement scrum-half for starting fly-half Andy Goode, with starting scrum-half Austin Healey switching to fly-half?

152. Going into the final stages of the game, the scores were level at 27–27. Who scored a drop goal in the 77th minute to put the French side three points ahead of the Tigers?

153. Who scored two tries for the Tigers in the 2001 Heineken Cup Final?

154. Who won the lineout that led to Austin Healey's break that led to Leicester's winning try in the 79th minute?

155. What was the final score in the 2001 Heineken Cup Final?

Chapter 11 – 1930s Tigers

156. Can you name the Tigers captain who was selected to tour Australasia with the 1930 British Isles party?

157. The first BBC radio broadcast of a Tigers game on 5 September 1930 saw Leicester beat which team 21–5 at Welford Road?

158. Tigers' game against which arch-rivals at Welford Road in September 1931 was the first occasion that an entire Leicester team was lettered?

159. How many Tigers were in the Leicestershire & East Midlands side that beat the 1931 touring Springboks – 7, 9 or 10?

160. Can you name the Tiger who captained the Leicestershire & East Midlands side against the Springboks in 1931?

161. Who scored two tries, set up two more and dropped a goal in a virtuoso performance against the Springboks in 1931?

162. How many spectators watched the Springboks in 1931, which has been called the greatest ever game played at Welford Road – 10,000, 20,000 or 25,000?

163. What was the final score in the 1931 game between the Leicestershire & East Midlands and the Springboks?

164. Can you name the President of the RFU in 1968–69 who made his Tigers debut in 1932 against Harlequins?

165. In 1933 who became the first home-produced Tiger to captain England?

166. Who became in 1933 the second Tigers player to score a hat-trick of tries against the Barbarians?

167. To raise cash during the 1930s recession what did the club start to sell on match days – scarves, matchday programmes or doughnuts?

168. In 1932 during the depression the unemployed were admitted to the Welford Road end on production of an unemployment card at a discount entrance fee of – 1d, 3d or 6d?

169. Which former Leicester captain, secretary and president dropped goals from over 40 yards in the 1930s, no mean feat given the heavy leather ball then in use?

170. In what year was a Supporters Club formed for fund raising – 1928, 1932 or 1934?

171. Name the Tiger's Russian Prince who went down in history for scoring one of the greatest tries of the time for England against the All Blacks in 1936 when he carved a diagonal path from his post on the right wing to score on the left.

172. Which former Newbold back scored four tries in Tigers 16–0 win against Blackheath in 1937–38?

173. Who topped Leicester's points chart in 1937–38 with 77?

174. Which local rivals did the Tigers beat for the first time for five years at Welford in November 1938?

175. Leicester's final game prior to the outbreak of World War II was a 10–23 defeat against which London-based club?

Chapter 12 – International Tigers

176. Who was the first England player to be capped 50 times?

177. Which Tiger who made his club debut in 1990 is one of the rare breed of players to have been caped for two different countries – Australia and Ireland?

178. Can you name the Tiger who on his international debut in 1963 led his Scotland team to a famous victory over France, kicking eight points in the 11–6 away win?

179. Which number eight scored two tries on his international debut in 1986, a feat not achieved by an England player since Harry Wilkinson in 1929?

180. How many Tigers played for England against Ireland in 1984?

181. Which four Tigers were in England's grand slam side of 1980?

182. Can you name the Irish international back-row forward who made over 100 appearances for the Tigers in 1942 became the first RAF officer to be promoted to the rank of air commodore?

183. Can you name the Tigers hooker who became an England selector in 1987 working alongside Geoff Cook and Roger Uttley and was assistant manager on the England tour to Argentina in 1990?

184. Can you name the Tiger who scored England's opening try in the 2008 Six Nations game against Wales, and managed another the following game against Italy?

185. Who made his England début against Canada on 2 June 2001 displacing Danny Grewcock from the side?

186. Which legendary Leicester centre won the first of his 32 caps for England in 1978 against Wales?

187. Martin Johnson made his England debut in 1993 against which country?

188. Who did Martin Johnson succeed as England's team manager on 1 July 2008?

189. Who scored England's opening try in the 2008 Six Nations game against Wales, and managed another the following game against Italy?

190. Which Tiger was named as a member of Martin Johnson's first England elite player squad ready for selection for the 2008–09 international season but was dropped before the start of the 2009 Six Nations?

191. Can you name England's leading try scorer (49) who played for the Tigers between 1983 and 1997?

192. Which former Tigers centre scored 31 tries for England?

193. Which Tiger retired after he was dropped from the England team during the 2004 Six Nations, citing that he wanted to spend more time with his family rather than fight for his place in the side?

194. Who was named as England Captain for the 2005 Six Nations match against Italy and Scotland, in the absence of Jason Robinson?

195. Name the former Tiger who succeeded Peter de Villiers as coach of South Africa's national team the Springboks on 27 January 2012 for a four-year term.

196. Who gained his first England cap against South Africa at Twickenham in 2008–09 and started the Heineken Cup Final for Tigers at the end of that season after kicking the sudden-death winning penalty in an historic shoot-out win over Cardiff Blues in the semi-finals?

197. How many times did Richard Cockerill play for England?

198. Which Tiger made his debut as a replacement in opening game of 2010 RBS Six Nations?

199. Which Tigers legend played in the 1998 and 1999 Five Nations and the 1999 World Cup, missing out on only two possible selections for England's 22 during his test career?

200. How many Tigers were named by England head coach Stuart Lancaster in his senior squad for the 2013 RBS Six Nations?

Chapter 13 – Anglo Welsh Cup

201. Sixteen clubs contest the Anglo-Welsh Cup annually. How many are Welsh – 2, 4 or 8?

202. Who were the augural winners of the Anglo-Welsh Cup in 2006?

203. Can you name the first Welsh club to reach the final of the Anglo-Welsh Cup?

204. How many times have the Leicester Tigers reached the final of the Anglo-Welsh Cup?

205. How many times have Leicester Tigers won the Anglo-Welsh Cup?

206. Leicester's first ever Anglo-Welsh Cup game played on 30 September 2005 was also their first defeat in the competition. Which Welsh club beat them 24–15?

207. Leicester reached the final of the Anglo-Welsh Cup for the first time in 2007. Which English club did they beat 29–19 in Cardiff?

208. The Leicester Tigers faced Ospreys in the final of the 2007 Anglo-Welsh Cup. In which Welsh city are Ospreys based?

209. Who scored two tries for the Tigers in their 41–35 win over the Ospreys in the 2007 Anglo-Welsh Cup Final?

210. Name the teenage fly half who landed four penalties as Leicester beat Bath to reach the LV= Cup (Anglo-Welsh) Final in 2012.

211. Which ground staged the 2012 LV= Cup Final?

212. Which local rivals did the Tigers beat 26-14 to win the LV= Cup in 2012?

213. Who scored three penalties for Leicester's opponents in the 2012 LV= Cup Final?

214. Can you name both Tigers try scorers in the 2012 LV= Cup Final?

215. Name the two teams who beat the Tigers in the LV= Cup competition in 2012-13.

Chapter 14 – 1940s Tigers

216. During the 1945–46 season it was decided to run two teams, the first to be called the Leicester Football Club. What was the second team called?

217. Who was the first post World War II Leicester captain?

218. The first game of the newly constructed club was played on 8 September 1945. It was the first game between the clubs since a rift some 15 years earlier. Can you identify Leicester's Welsh opponents?

219. In 1946 Leicester began their old players' membership scheme. What was the qualification for membership?

220. Name the fly-half who made his Tigers debut in 1946 whose grandfather founded the South African regional team, the Swifts.

221. Can you name Leicester's first replacement who took over from J.C.K. Campbell at Blackheath in December 1946 after arriving late for the game?

222. Which Welsh club scored 50 points against the Tigers in 1947?

223. Leicester's biggest win in the 1940s was a 32–3 victory against which London-based club on 6 Mar 1948?

224. Who was Leicester's captain from 1947–49 who later became County RFU President for three years?

225. Who was the Tigers leading points scorer in the 1940s?

Chapter 15 – World Cup Tigers

226. In what year was the first Rugby World Cup tournament held?

227. Name the Leicester legend who played in the 1987, 1991 and 1995 World Cups for England.

228. In 2003, England won the Rugby World Cup by defeating Australia in the final. Who captained England to victory?

229. How many Leicester Tigers players were in England's starting line-up for the 2003 Rugby Union World Cup Final?

230. Can you name the Tigers player who replaced Richard Hill in the 83rd minute of the 2003 World Cup Final?

231. Which Tigers player scored five tries for England in the 2003 Rugby World Cup Finals tournament?

232. Name the Tigers' World Cup bronze medalist with Argentina in 2007, who was named in the Sky Sports Dream Team at the Premiership awards in 2008–09 and ended that season with appearances in both Tests against England.

233. He was one of only four players to have started both the 2003 and 2007 RWC Finals, the other three being Jonny Wilkinson, Jason Robinson and Phil Vickery?

234. Who was the only player to play every minute of England's 2007 Rugby World Cup campaign culminating in their narrow loss in the Final?

235. Who flew home from Australia during the 2003 Rugby World Cup for the birth of his first child, daughter Eve, re-joining the squad days later, and played in England's victory over Uruguay?

236. Name the World Cup finalist in 2007 after receiving a late call-up, who joined Tigers from Newcastle Falcons in 2008 and became the first player since Dusty Hare in 1977 to top the club's points-scoring charts in his debut season?

237. Which Tiger scored a try for England in the 2003 World Cup quarter final tie against Wales?

238. Who coached Argentina in the 2003 World Rugby Cup?

239. Which former Tigers player and coach scored all of South Africa's points, including the famous dramatic winning drop goal, against New Zealand in the 1995 Rugby World Cup Final?

240. Who was England's forwards' coach during the 2007 World Cup?

Chapter 16 – Heineken Cup Winners

Name the Heineken Cup winners

Winners	Season	Runners-up
241.	1995–96	Cardiff
242.	1997–98	Brive
243.	1998–99	Colomiers
244.	1999–2000	Munster
245.	2002–03	Perpignan
246.	2003–04	Toulouse
247.	2004–05	Stade Francais
248.	2007–08	Toulouse
249.	2010–11	Northampton Saints
250.	2011–12	Ulster

Chapter 17 – 1950s Tigers

251. Can you name the Leicester centre who distinguished himself against Nuneaton in 1950 by scoring in ever possible way in a 16–8 win?

252. Which England international back, who only made eight appearances for the Tigers in 1950–51 season, later became the secretary of the RFU?

253. Can you name both of Leicester's ever-presents in 1950–51?

254. Name the scrum-half that captained the Tigers between 1950–53, who later became a member of the East Midlands Referee Society.

255. The Tigers first TV appearance, a 14–0 win against London Scottish on the Richmond Athletic Ground, took place in what year – 1951, 1956 or 1959?

256. Can you name the Leicester prop of the early 1950s, who played 17 successive games for England, five times as captain, which included the triple crown season of 1953–54?

257. Which club won at Welford Road for the first time since 1895–96 in November 1953?

258. Who scored three tries for the Barbarians in their 39–11 hammering of Leicester in 1953?

259. Major Albert Chilton was appointed the club's first paid official in 1954. What was his annual salary?

260. Leicester Football Club beat which Welsh side 8–5 in March 1955 at St Helens for the first time in 31 years?

261. What was disbanded at the Tigers annual meeting in 1955?

262. Can you name the legendary Tigers flanker who made his Leicester debut in the opening fixture of the 1955–56 season against Bedford?

263. Who passed the 500 points mark for the Tigers in a game against the Old Blues in 1955–56?

264. The Tigers first game on a Sunday played on 18 November 1956 was a 3–23 loss against which club in Dublin?

265. Clocks were unveiled in October 1959 on the stands at Welford Road as a tribute to which former Tigers Honorary Secretary?

266. Who played 16 successive games on Scotland's wing and would have enjoyed a longer career at Leicester but for a pre-season training accident in 1959, when his knee was so badly damaged in a tackle by David Senior that he never played rugby again?

267. Can you name the Leicester centre of the 1950s who coached England between 1972–74?

268. Which Irish international, who would later become chief executive of H.J. Heinz Company, made his Leicester debut against Northampton in 1958?

269. Can you name the durable second-row forward, who in the 1950s established a then club record of 103 consecutive games for the Tigers?

270. Which full-back established a post war Leicester record for points scored (145) in the 1958–89 season?

Chapter 18 – What Year – Rugby Union

271. In what year was the Rugby Football Union formed – 1871, 1876 or 1888?

272. In what year did the Five Nations become the Six Nations Championship – 1999, 2000 or 2003?

273. In what year was Rugby Union declared an "open" game, and professionalism was sanctioned by the code's governing body – the International Rugby Board – 1993, 1995 or 1997?

274. In what year was the first Rugby World Cup tournament held – 1983, 1987 or 1991?

275. In what year did Rugby Union first appear in the summer Olympics – 1900, 1904 or 1908?

276. In what year was the world's first and oldest "football club" the Guy's Hospital Football Club, founded in London by old boys from Rugby School – 1823, 1833 or 1843?

277. In what year was the first recognised international match, played between England and Scotland, at Raeburn Place, Edinburgh – 1869, 1871 or 1876?

278. In what year was the value of a try increased from four to five points – 1986, 1989 or 1992?

279. In what year was Mini rugby invented – 1965, 1970 or 1980?

280. In what year was Twickenham opened – 1907, 1909 or 1919?

Chapter 19 – 1960s Tigers

281. Who scored the most tries for the Tigers during the 1960s?

282. Who made the most appearances for the Tigers during the 1960s?

283. Who scored the most points (551) for the Tigers during the 1960s?

284. Leicester Tigers first game under floodlights, was a 9–19 defeat in February 1960, played at which Welsh club?

285. Who was elected captain of the Leicester Tigers for the 1960–61 season?

286. Can you name the club the Tigers traditionally played in first or second fixture of each season during the 1960s?

287. Who played his 300th game for Leicester against Newport in February 1961?

288. How many tries did David Matthews score for Leicester in 1960–61 – 9, 11 or 15?

289. Whose run of 109 successive first team appearances for the Tigers came to an end against Blackheath in December 1963?

290. In which year were floodlights used for the first time at Welford Road – 1962, 1964 or 1966?

291. Why didn't the Tigers play a game for 12 weeks during 1962–63 season?

292. There was no admission charge for Leicester's away game at Harlequins in March 1963. How many fans watched the greatly anticipated encounter between two of England's most successful clubs – 300, 3,000 or 30,000?

293. What was presented to the club at the 1963 annual meeting by former player of the 1920s Charles Cramphorn – tiger skin, metal goal posts or silver plated rugby ball?

294. What unwelcome guest appeared in one scrum during the 1964 Barbarians game – dead rat, streaker or dog?

295. Who scored a hat-trick of tries for the Tigers against the Barbarians in 1965?

296. Can you name the England centre who tragically broke his neck in a tackle on Ian MacRae during the combined Midland and Home Counties XV match against the All Blacks at Welford Road in October 1967?

297. Which Leicester legend took up a coaching role at the club in 1967?

298. Which Leicester reserve was sent off 10 seconds before the start of the game at Iffley Road, Oxford in 1969?

299. Who scored his 100th Tigers try against Bristol in 1968?

300. Which Leicester legend made his Tigers debut against Cambridge University in November 1969?

Chapter 20 - Welford Road

301. Welford Road largest designated club rugby stadium in England. True or False?

302. The new Members' Stand at Welford Road was officially opened in 1918 for the Tigers first home game for three and a half years. Who were Leicester's opponents?

303. Can you name the South African side the Tigers played in November 1995 to mark the official opening of the new 3,000 seat Alliance & Leicester stand?

304. Who was the first player to have made 300 appearances at Welford Road?

305. The Tigers played how many games at the 'Reccy', later known as Nelson Mandela Park?

306. Leicester Tigers played one home game at Covert Lane because Welford Road was being used for the Midlands Counties game against the touring New Zealanders in October 1967. Which Leicester rugby club are based at Covert Lane?

307. What was the capacity of Welford Road in 1913?

308. In 2004, the Tigers announced a plan to abandon Welford Road in favour of a ground share at the Walkers Stadium with the city's main football club, Leicester City FC. True or False?

309. What is the current capacity (2013) of Welford Road Stadium?

310. Who did Tonga beat 28–25 in a Rugby World Cup game hosted at Welford Road in October 1999?

311. The Caterpillar Stand opened on 19 September 2009 with a capacity crowd watching a match between Leicester Tigers and?

312. The official opening ceremony of the Caterpillar Stand took place in November 2009 when the Tigers played which side?

313. What is the capacity of Welford Road's Caterpillar Stand?

314. What is the name of the stand located on the South side of Welford Road and home to The Mark and ABC Bar?

315. Since 2002 for men, and 2004 for women, Welford Road Stadium has hosted the annual Varsity match between which two universities?

316. Who scored his 154th try for Leicester overtaking Harry Wilkinson as the club's leading try scorer, in the home game to mark the official opening of the new Members Stand at Welford Road, against the 4th Leicester Regiment, in December 1918?

317. In April 1997 the Tigers beat Wasps 18–12 in front of a record English league crowd at Welford Road. What was the attendance that day – 17,000, 23,000 or 29,000?

318. Who set a club record 43 points in the 95–6 trouncing of Birmingham at Welford Road in September 1986?

319. In 2002–3 how many times did the Tigers play to a capacity crowd at Welford Road – 9, 11 or 13?

320. Who headlined the first pop concert held at Welford Road Stadium in July 2010?

Chapter 21 – 1970s Tigers

321. Who scored the most tries (151) for the Tigers during the 1970s?

322. Who made the most appearances (330) for the Tigers during the 1970s?

323. Who scored the most points (1,093) for the Tigers during the 1970s?

324. Who played 349 games for the Tigers plus 41 England and seven Lions caps between 1969 and 1985?

325. At the start of the 1970s the Tigers had approximately how many members – 600, 1,200 or 1,800?

326. Attendance at Leicester Tigers games at the start of the 1970s was typically less than 1,000. True or False?

327. Can you name the Leicester legend who as a 17-year-old played for Midland Counties East against Fiji at Welford Road in November 1970?

328. Can you name one of the best line out exponents for Leicester in the 1960s and 1970s who also played football for Leicester City and international basketball?

329. Leicester's first 'modern' cup tie was a 3–10 defeat against which club in the first round of the RFU Knockout Cup in November 1971?

330. Who scored three tries for Leicester against the Barbarians in 1971?

331. At the start of the 1972–73 season Leicester captain Graham Williams and coach Chalkie White set a target of 30 wins and 1,000 points. Did the club meet these targets?

332. Name the local centre who played 23 times for the Tigers in 1972–73 scoring 200 points, all but 12 from the boot.

333. Who scored 29 tries for Leicester in 1972–73?

334. Who broke Sid Penny's Tigers appearance record with his 492nd First XV game at Broughton Park in April 1973?

335. Name the England international loose head prop who made his Leicester debut in September 1974 and went on to gain four John Players Cup winners medals.

336. Can you name the two Welshmen who scored tries in the Tigers 11–10 win at Llanelli in 1974?

337. In 1974–75 which Leicester legend established a world record of 25 drop goals in a season while playing for Wakefield?

338. Who became the youngest Tiger to win his player's tie which was awarded after playing against the Barbarians in 1975 at the age of 17 years 305 days – only 112 days after his debut?

339. Who played in goal for Notts County and made over 150 appearances as second row forward for the Tigers between 1968 and 1975?

340. Can you name the legendary full-back who scored 22 points on his Leicester debut in 1976 against Oxford University?

341. Which 'Ash' did the Tigers beat 45--3 in September 1976?

342. Which Tiger was selected for the British Lions tour of New Zealand and Fiji in 1977 as number two hooker to Bobby Windsor?

343. Who scored his 1,000th point for the Tigers with his first try two tries in a 23–17 win over Harlequins in September 1977?

344. The Tigers reach the final of the John Player Cup in January 1978. Who did they beat in R1?

345. What are Dusty Hare's Christian names?

346. The Tigers received home draws all the way through to the 1978 John Player Cup Final. True or False?

347. Can you name the Tigers' captain who broke two ribs in the quarter-final game?

348. Can you name which local rivals Leicester beat 20–11 in the quarter-final with Joyce and Duggan scoring tries and Hare and Dodge sharing four penalties?

349. Who did Leicester beat 25–16 to reach the 1978 John Player Cup Final?

350. Who were the Tigers first opponents in a Twickenham final?

351. What was the final score in the 1978 John Player Cup Final?

352. Who was Leicester's only scorer in the 1978 John Player Cup Final?

353. The attendance at the 1978 Cup Final was double the previous highest for a cup final. How many fans watched Leicester's first game at Twickenham – 12,000, 18,000 or 24,000?

354. Can you name the Leicester legend who in the second game of the 1978–79 season completed 100 games for the club whilst still aged only 20?

355. Can you name the BBC Radio Leicester commentator who played in the Tigers' first John Player Cup Final?

356. Who was elected captain at the start of the 1978–79 season?

357. How many club members did the Tigers have at the end of 1979 – 1,000, 2,000 or 5,000?

358. Can you name the England B fly-half who joined the Tigers from Moseley in September 1978?

359. Who ended the 1978–79 season as the Tiger's highest points scorer with 304?

360. Leicester knocked out Northampton and Broughton Park to reach the quarter-final stage of the John Player Cup in 1979. Who did they beat 22–12 to reach the last four of the Cup?

361. The Tigers utterly overwhelmed Wasps away from home to reach the 1979 John Player Cup Final for the second successive season. What was the final score witnessed by millions of BBC viewers – 32–3, 43–7 or 53–9?

362. Two Tigers players scored two tries in the 1979 John Player Cup semi-final. Can you name them both?

363. Who did Moseley beat 6–3 to face Leicester in the 1979 John Player Cup Final?

364. Who captained the Leicester Tigers in the 1979 John Player Cup Final?

365. What was the attendance at the 1979 John Player Cup Final – 8,000, 18,000 or 24,000?

366. Who dropped a goal in the 8th minute of the 1979 John Player Cup Final?

367. Who scored the first try in the 1979 John Player Cup Final ?

368. What was the half-time score in the 1979 John Player Cup Final?

369. Who scored the decisive try for Leicester with just three minutes remaining in the 1979 John Player Cup Final?

370. Who scored his 150th try for the Tigers in the 55–3 victory against Headingley in 1979?

Chapter 22 – 2002 Heineken Cup Final

371. Leicester became the first club to retain the Heineken Cup in 2002 by beating Irish Province Munster. What was the final score?

372. Who was Leicester's captain in the 2002 Heineken Cup Final?

373. Who captained Munster in the 2002 Heineken Cup Final?

374. Which stadium hosted the 2002 Heineken Cup Final?

375. Leicester almost got off to the perfect start in the 2002 Heineken Cup Final when who raced over with just one minute on the clock, only for referee Joel Jutge to bring the Midlanders back for an illegal push on John Kelly?

376. Who ran over after a dismal throw in at the lineout by Frankie Sheahan in the first quarter of the 2002 Heineken Cup Final – only for it to be again ruled out by the referee?

377. Name the scorer of the first try in the 2002 Heineken Cup Final.

378. Can you name the scorer of all of Munster's points in the 2002 Heineken Cup Final?

379. Who was voted Man of the Match in the 2002 Heineken Cup Final?

380. Who produced a delightful dummy to score Leicester's second try?

Chapter 23 – British Lions & Tigers

381. In what year did the British and Irish Lions make their first tour?

382. Who was the first Tiger to captain the British Lions?

383. Which place kicker scored nine conversions and six penalty goals in 16 games (five of them Tests) during the British Lions tour of Australasia in 1950?

384. Martin Johnson was selected to captain the 1997 British Lions tour of South Africa. Who managed the Lions on the tour?

385. Who withdrew from the Tigers side that played in the 1983 John Player Cup Final because he did not want to risk his place in the British Lions tour party that year?

386. Whose final top-flight rugby match was the Lions first test against New Zealand in 2005?

387. How many of the five Tigers players selected for the 2001 British and Irish Lions tour to Australia can you name?

388. Can you name the Leicester Tigers forward who played for the Lions during the 1977 tour to New Zealand?

389. Who was the first player ever to captain the British Lions on two separate tours, when he leads them in Australia?

390. Name the Tigers flanker called up to the squad by coach Ian McGeehan for the Lions 2009 tour of South Africa as a replacement for the banned Alan Quinlan.

391. Who scored a try on his Lions debut against the Golden Lions in June 2009 and added two tries in his first Test against South Africa to announce his arrival on the world scene?

392. How many times was Dean Richards capped by the British Lions – 6, 8 or 9?

393. Which Tiger led a Great Britain team to a 10–0 winning series against Argentina in 1930?

394. Who was selected for his second Lions tour, to New Zealand in 2004 and went on to captain the team from the second minute onwards as Brian O'Driscoll was injured in a notorious spear tackle incident?

395. Can you identify the six (6) Leicester Tigers players named in the Lions squad that toured Australia in 2013?

Chapter 24 – 1980s Tigers

396. Who scored the most tries (156) for the Tigers during the 1980s?

397. Who made the most appearances (309) for the Tigers during the 1980s?

398. Who scored the most points (3,423) for the Tigers during the 1980s?

399. Which Tiger, winner of seven7 Lions caps, made his last appearance for England in March 1984 against Wales?

400. Leicester Tigers topped the RFU Merit Table in 1980. Can you name Leicester's local rivals who finished the season in second place?

401. Can you identify the Northern Merit Table leaders who were the Tigers round one John Player Cup opponents in January 1980?

402. Can you name the four Tigers who played in England's Grand Slam winning side of 1980?

403. Which club based at the Reddings were the Tigers round two John Player Cup opponents in 1980?

404. Who broke Harold Day's record Tigers career points aggregate with his 1,152nd point, kicked on the day that Leicester retained the John Player Cup with a 21–9 victory over London Irish at Twickenham in April 1980?

405. Who registered 30 points for the Tigers against Harlequins in September 1980 from two tries, three penalty goals, five conversions and a dropped goal?

406. Which club did the Tigers beat in the semi-finals to secure a third successive John Player Cup Final appearance in 1980?

407. Who did the Tigers beat in the 1980 John Player Cup Final?

408. What was the final score in the 1980 John Player Cup Final?

409. Who scored two dropped goals for the Tigers in the 1980 John Player Cup Final?

410. Two players scored more than 100 points for Leicester in 1979–80?

411. Which two Tigers players were picked for the British Lions 1980 summer tour of South Africa?

412. Can you name the Tiger who joined the 1980 British Lions summer tour party when the Welsh centre David Richards, was injured?

413. To honour the centenary of the club's foundation in 1980, Leicester become the first English club side to embark on a tour to the Southern Hemisphere. True or False?

414. Which team slaughtered the Tigers 46–10 in February 1981 – Coventry, Blackheath or London Welsh?

415. At the end of full-time what was the score in the 1981 John Player Cup semi-final tie between Leicester and London Scottish?

416. Who settled the semi-final tie in Leicester's favour with two dropped goals in extra-time?

417. Tigers won the John Player Cup for a third successive season in 1981. Can you name the club they beat 22–15 in the Final?

418. The 1981 John Player Cup Final was whose last as Leicester's captain?

419. Approximately how many of the 24,000 fans at the 1981 John Player Cup Final were from Leicester?

420. Can you name Leicester's try scorers in the 1981 John Player Cup Final?

421. After winning the John Player Cup for the third successive season in 1981 Leicester were allowed to keep the original trophy which is now on display at the Clubhouse. True or False?

422. What was the venue for Leicester Football Club's Centenary Dinner in April 1980?

423. How much did it cost to watch the Tigers play Australia in the members Stand at Welford Road in November 1981 – £1.25, £2.75 or £4?

424. What was the final score in the game between the Tigers and Australia in 1981?

425. Which side knocked the Tigers out of the John Player Cup in 1982?

426. Which Leicester number 8 legend made his Tigers debut against Neath in April 1982?

427. Who scored thee tries in the Tigers 36–16 win against the Barbarians in 1982?

428. Can you name the first Tigers player for five years to be sent off, for retaliating against Bath flanker Roger Spurrell in 1983?

429. Leicester lost the 1983 John Player Cup Final 28–22 against which team?

430. Can you name which Tigers player made his 207th and final appearance for the club in the 1983 John Player Cup Final?

431. Who scored the first try of the 1983 John Player Cup Final that took Leicester past the 1,000 points for the season for the first time?

432. Which Tigers player underwent a five (5) hour operation to remove a blood clot on the brain after a clash with a Bristol player during the 1983 John Player Cup Final?

433. The Tigers established a new club record of how many successive wins from the start of the 1983–84 season – 31, 47 or 57?

434. Which serving RAF officer joined the Tigers in 1983?

435. Why did Leicester City Council ban the Tigers from using Welford Road Recreation Ground for 12 months in August 1984?

436. Who announced his retirement from international rugby in September 1984, having played at the time more games for England (25) than any previous encumbent?

437. How many Tigers players appeared in the England side that faced Ireland at Twickenham in 1984?

438. Leicester Football Club signed a five year deal with which brewery in 1984, designed to offset the costs of refurbishing Welford Road?

439. Which England international Tiger with 241 games under his belt turned 'professional' when he joined the newly formed Rugby League side Sheffield Eagles in 1984?

440.   Who scored four tries for the Tigers in a 43–4 victory against Bristol in round three of the John Player Cup in January 1985?

441.   Can you name the Tigers player who 'scored in every way in a game' twice during 1985?

442.   Can you name the first side to win a John Player Cup tie at Welford Road when they beat Leicester 8–10 in 1986?

443.   Who set a club record 43 points in the 95–6 trouncing of Birmingham at Welford Road in September 1986?

444.   How many tries did the Tigers score against the Barbarians in 1987– 3, 6 or 9?

445.   Who became the 26th Tiger to play 300 games for the club, in the game against Ballymena in April 1988?

446.   In the penultimate game of the 1987–88 season, which club did the Tigers slaughter 65–0 at Welford Road?

447.   Can you name the two Tigers who scored a hat-trick of tries in Leicester's 65–0 win in April 1988?

448.   Who dropped a club record four goals in a game at Liverpool St Helens in the third round of the Cup in January 1989?

449.   Which Leicester legendary lock made his Tigers debut against the RAF in February 1989?

450.   Who dropped his 30th cup goal for the Tigers to in the semi-final to ensure another meeting with the club's nemesis, Bath in the 1989 Pilkington Cup Final?

451. What was the world record attendance that watched the 1989 Pilkington Cup Final – 58,000, 68,000 or 78,000?

452. What was the final score in the 1989 Pilkington Cup Final?

453. Who scored all of Leicester's points in the 1989 Pilkington Cup Final?

454. Bath's victory against the Tigers in the 1989 Pilkington Cup Final gave them English rugby's first 'double'. True or False?

455. Can you name Leicester's captain from 1983–85, who retired from first class rugby at the end of the season having played more than 300 games for the club?

Chapter 25 – Home Grounds

Can you identify the professional English rugby clubs based at the following stadia?

456. Recreation Ground

457. Allianz Park

458. Franklin's Gardens

459. Kassam Stadium

460. Sandy Park

461. Adams Park

462. Sixways Stadium

463. Kingsholm Stadium

464. The Stoop

465. Madejski Stadium

Chapter 26 – Author Author!

Can you identify the authors of the following books?

466. Deano

467. Winning

468. Flying Wing

469. Size Doesn't Matter

470. The Outsider

471. My Life in Rugby

472. Leading from the Front

473. Lions, Tigers and Roses

474. In Your Face: A Rugby Odyssey

475. Will – The Autobiography

Chapter 27 – Left Leicester

Which clubs did the following players leave Leicester Tigers to play for?

476.   George Beamish

477.   Alfred Hind

478.   Marcus Rose

479.   Bob Sterling

480.   Will Greenwood

481.   Dan Hipkiss

482.   Leon Lloyd

483.   Lewis Moody

484.   Sam Vesty

485.   Tom Varndell

486.   Leo Cullen

487.   Dave Lougheed

488.   Tony O'Reilly

489.   Craig Joiner

490. Billy Twelvetress

491. Ollie Smith

492. Tom Youngs

493. George Skivington

494. Horacio Agulla

495. Tony Underwood

Chapter 28 – 1990s – Tigers

496. How many times did Leicester Football Club win the Premiership during the 1990s?

497. How many times were Leicester Tigers crowned European Champions in the 1990s?

498. How many times did the Tigers win the English Cup during the 1990s?

499. Who scored the most tries (85) for the Tigers during the 1990s?

500. Who made the most appearances for the Tigers (246) during the 1990s?

501. Who scored the most points (2,280) for the Tigers during the 1990s?

502. Who damaged his shoulder so badly in the first league game of the 1989–90 season at Wasps that it effectively ended his season?

503. Who was Leicester's captain for the vast majority of the 1989–90 season?

504. Who scored five tries in his 34th international for England in 1990, equaling the record set by 'Dan' Lambert in 1907 for one match?

505. Who made is 350th Tigers appearance against Saracens in 1990?

506. Can you name the wing who scored five tries in Leicester's 70–4 win against the RAF in February 1990?

507. In what League position did the Tigers finish in the Courage League in 1990 season?

508. What was Leicester's third team called, which was replaced by the under-21s side in 1991? Swifts

509. Can you name the club's first full-time coach?

510. What was initial annual salary of the Tigers first full-time coach – £12,000, £15,000 or £20,000?

511. Can you name the scorer of 947 points for the Tigers who played his final game for the club away at Bath in April 1990?

512. Who scored a record breaking 439 points for the Tigers in 1989–90 season?

513. Barry Evans, scorer of 158 tries for the Tigers, left Leicester to join which club in 1991?

514. Leicester inflicted Bath's first home Cup feat since 1982 in 1990. What was the final score – 0–3, 0–12 or 0–21?

515. Can you name the Roehampton–based club, who beat Leicester in the Courage League in October 1990?

516. Who scored a controversial penalty for Wasps to knock the Tigers out of the Pilkington Cup 13–14 at Welford Road in January 1991?

517. Who was voted Whitbread's Rugby World Player of the Year in 1990–91?

518. The Tigers achieved their record points total in a game by demolishing Liverpool St Helens in April 1992 by what score at Welford Road – 100–0, 110–0 or 120–0?

519. Who scored six tries in Leicester's thrashing of Liverpool St Helens in 1992?

520. Who on joining the Tigers in 1992 established himself as the B of the "ABC club"?

521. From 1992–93 season, how many point were awarded for a try?

522. Who did Leicester thrash 76–0 in quarter-finals of the Pilkington Cup in February 1993?

523. Who scored a hat-trick of tries for Leicester in the 1993 quarter-final Pilkington Cup tie?

524. For the first time in the history of the English Cup, Welford Road was sold out for the 1993 Pilkington Cup semi-final tie against which local rivals?

525. What was the final score in the 1993 Pilkington Cup semi-final tie at Welford Road in 1993?

526. Leicester's opponents in the 1993 Pilkington Cup Final were Harlequins. Who did they beat in the semi-final?

527. The 1993 Pilkington Cup Final was the last game for which English flanker into whose shoes Neil Back was trying so desperately to fill?

528. On the morning of the 1993 Pilkington Cup Final which England hooker withdrew from the game with a groin strain?

529. Who were Leicester's "ABC club" in the 1993 Pilkington Cup Final?

530. Leicester fans outnumbered Harlequins fans by what proportion at the 1993 Pilkington Cup Final – 2 to 1, 4 to 1 or 6 to 1?

531. Who was named by Whitbread/*Rugby World and Post* as the most promising player in 1993 shortly after his try-scoring display for the Tigers in the 1993 Pilkington Cup Final?

532. What was the final score in the 1993 Pilkington Cup Final?

533. Tigers won the Courage League for a second time after beating Bristol 17–3 in front of how many spectators at Welford Road in April 1995 – 13,000, 15,000 or 17,000?

534. Who was appointed the Tigers Director of Rugby in May 1996?

535. Who was Leicester's top try scorer in 1995–96 with 16 tries?

536. Who in 1996 became at the time the youngest Leicester Tigers player to play a League game for the club aged 18 years and 94 days?

537. The Courage League had been very popular but the league really took off when which organisation took over the title sponsorship of Division One in 1996?

538. Who left Harlequins and moved to Leicester Tigers in 1996 because the presence of England centre Will Carling meant he could not get first team rugby?

539. Why was Neil Back banned from rugby for six months in 1996?

540. How many Leicester players were named in the British Lions squad to tour South Africa in 1997 – 2, 4 or 6?

541. Who did the Tigers beat 18–12 in front of a record English League crowd of 17,000 at Welford Road in April 1997?

542. Which Scottish team was demolished by the Tigers 90–19 in a Heineken Cup Pool Game in 1997?

543. Can you name the South African fly half who scored 896 points for the Tigers between 1997 and 1999?

544. Who took over as the Tiger's Rugby Manager in February 1998?

545. Tigers clinched a third league title in 1999 when they took the Allied Dunbar Premiership with a 21–12 victory against which team at Kingston Park?

Chapter 29 – Join Leicester

Which clubs did the following players leave to play for the Leicester Tigers?

546. Robin Cowling

547. Les Cusworth

548. Bernard Gadney

549. Brian Hall

550. Dusty Hare

551. Austin Healey

552. Tim Stimpson

553. Joel Stransky

554. Mefin Davies

555. Ken Jones

556. Alesana Tuilagi

557. Daryl Gibson

558. Julien Dupuy

559. Julian White

560. Rory Underwood

561. Anthony Allen

562. George Chuter

563. Horacio Agulla

564. Ramiro Pez

565. Benjamin Kayser

Chapter 30 – What Year – Tigers

566. In what year were floodlights first used at Welford Road, for a game against a Midlands XV, won 31–8 by Tigers - 1952, 1958 or 1964?

567. In what year did Welford Road host a Rugby World Cup game for the second time as Tonga shocked Italy 28–25 – 1987, 1993 or 1999?

568. In what year did the earliest reference to the now famous Tiger nickname appear in the *Leicester Daily Post* stating "the Tiger stripes were keeping well together." – 1881, 1885 or 1894?

569. In what year did Martin Johnson become the first player ever to captain the British Lions on two separate tours – 1999, 2000 or 2001?

570. In what year did the Leicester Tigers became a plc after a successful share issue raised a vital funds – 1995, 1997 or 1999?

571. In what year did Leicester forwards start to regularly wear letters as a means of identification – 1919, 1921 or 1926?

572. In what year was Tony Russ appointed first full-time coach of the Leicester Tigers – 1989, 1990 or 1991?

573. In what year did Leicester wear their famous scarlet, green and white colours for the first time in a vertical stripe formation – 1883, 1891 or 1901?

574. In what year was an 18 foot electronic scoreboard unveiled at Welford Road – 1989, 1993 or 1997?

575. In what year did the Tigers play at Wembley Stadium for the first time – 2001, 2009 or 2012?

576. In what year was extra-time first used to decide the winner in a Tigers' game – 1891, 1931 or 1996?

577. In what year was the 'new' clubhouse opened at Welford Road for the game against Stratford-upon-Avon, containing for the first time dressing rooms on the ground – 1909, 1919 or 1929?

578. In what year did Leicester Tigers make history in their Heineken Cup semi-final against Cardiff Blues when a place kicking competition was required to decide the outcome for the first time – 2009, 2010 or 2011?

579. In what year did Leicester become the first English club side to embark on a tour to the Southern Hemisphere where they play six games in Australia and Fiji, only losing the opening game to Queensland – 1980, 1985 or 1990?

580. In what year did hooker George Chuter becomes the first man to reach 250 Premiership appearances – 2009, 2010 or 2012?

Chapter 31 – 1987–88 Courage League

581. How many teams competed in the Courage League National Division One in 1987–88?

582. There was no fixture list in the inaugural Courage League campaign; the teams arranged fixtures amongst themselves. One match would count between each of the twelve teams involved. True or False?

583. How many points were awarded for a win – 2, 3 or 4?

584. How many points were awarded for a loss – 0, 1 or 2?

585. Leicester first game in the Courage League was against England's acknowledged top club, merit table champions and cup holders. Can you identify the Tigers first Courage National Division One League opponents?

586. Leicester were confirmed as the inaugural Courage National Division One League champions with a 39–15 victory over which team?

587. How many games did the Tigers play in winning the Courage National Division One League Championship in 1988 – 10, 14 or 18?

588. Can you name the side Leicester beat 21–3 to go top of the Courage League for the first time in 1987?

589. Who was the first Leicester player to score a drop goal in the Courage National Division One League?

590. Leicester scored more than 40 points against only one side in the Courage League National Division One in 1987–88. Can you identify the Tigers unlucky opponents?

591. Who were the only side to beat the Tigers in the Courage League National Division One in 1987–88?

592. Who finished runners-up in the Courage League National Division One in 1988?

593. Which Courage League National Division One team did the Tigers not play in their Championship winning campaign in 1988?

594. Can you identify the 1987–88 Courage League National Division One club who played their home games at Ireland Avenue?

595. Which club lost all its 1987–88 Courage League National Division One fixtures and was relegated to Division Two?

Chapter 32 – 2000s – Tigers

596. How many times did Leicester Football Club win the Premiership between 2000 and 2009?

597. How many times were Leicester Tigers crowned European Champions between 2000 and 2009?

598. How many times did the Tigers win the English Cup between 2000 and 2009?

599. Who was voted both Leicester Tigers' and Allied Dunbar's Player of the Season in 2000?

600. The bonus point system was introduced for the 2000–01. How many tries did a team have to score in a game to be awarded a bonus point?

601. What was the maximum number of points a team could gain from one match?

602. Who were the first club to beat the Tigers in the Premiership in 2000–01?

603. Who did the Tigers draw with in the Premiership in September 2000?

604. Which former Tigers player's match-winning try to defeat Brive, in the European Shield quarter-final on 27 January 2001, was voted the Harlequins; 2000–01 'Try of the Year'?

605. Who did the Tigers slaughter 56–15 at Welford Road in a Premiership game in February 2001?

606. Tigers took a third Premiership crown in a row when Bath beat Wasps at the Rec, an hour or so after the Tigers had demolished which team 51–7 at Welford Road in March 2001?

607. Leicester claimed the inaugural Zurich Championship crown when they beat which team 22–10 in the final at Twickenham in May 2001?

608. Halfway through the 2001–02 season, with Leicester odds-on to win their fourth title in succession, it was decided that the winners of the playoffs would be crowned champions. After a public outcry at moving the goalposts halfway through the tournament, this was not followed through. True or False?

609. Who won the eight team Zurich Championship play-offs in 2001–02?

610. With the referee distracted on the other side of the scrum, which Tiger illegally swatted the ball from Munster scrum-half Peter Stringer's hands during the 2002 Heineken Final before the put-in and Leicester won possession and cleared the ball?

611. Can you name the fly-half who left the Tigers in 2002 to join Saracens only to return to Welford Road in 2003?

612. Who was named as the Tigers Members' Player of the Year 2001–02, and was a nominee for the Zurich Premiership Player of the Year?

613. The Leicester Tigers won the Orange Cup in 2002. Who did they beat 14–13?

614. Tigers U21s enjoyed a successful 2002–03 season winning the Zurich U21s League title. How many games did they lose in 2002–03?

615. Name the All Black who was voted the Players' Player of the Season 2002–03?

616. A fourth consecutive Premiership for the Tigers was wrapped up with a 20–10 victory over which team at Welford Road on 13 April 2002?

617. How many games were the Tigers unbeaten at home in a period that stretched from 30 December 1997 to 30 November 2002?

618. Who took over the Tigers captaincy in 2003-04?

619. Rugby World Cup call-ups wrecked havoc with the Tigers during 2003–04 when they lost eight members of their pack to the tournament. How many defeats did the Tigers suffer in their first 13 Zurich Premiership games of the 2003–4 season?

620. Leicester Tigers qualified for the 2003-04 edition of the Heineken Cup with a thrilling extra time victory over which club at Franklin's Gardens, Northampton to pick up the Zurich Wildcard?

621. Which Leicester Tiger finished the 2005–06 Guinness Premiership regular season, top of the try list with 14?

622. Who was appointed Director of Rugby for Harlequins Rugby Football Club in May 2005 following their relegation from the Zurich Premiership in the 2004–05 season and led them back to the Premiership at the first attempt, in a season where they lost only one league game?

623. Can you name the Tigers head coach who returned to Australia in 2007?

624. Name the Tigers Players' Player of the Season in 2003–04 and again in 2007–08.

625. Who became the club's youngest-ever league player with his debut in the closing seconds of a defeat at Bristol in April 2007 and came off the bench in the 2008 Guinness Premiership Final win over Gloucester before his 18th birthday?

626. Despite reaching two finals (EDF Energy and Guinness Premiership) who was sacked from his job as Head Coach at Leicester on 6 June 2008 due to poor results, after just one season at the club?

627. Who injured his achilles in the 2008–09 Heineken Cup semi-final game against Cardiff Blues – minutes before professional rugby's first ever sudden-death kicking competition?

628. Who tendered his resignation as the Tigers Head Coach on 29 January 2009?

629. Who scored the Tigers only try in their historic win over World Champions South Africa in 2009?

630. Who became acting head coach in 2009 and led the Tigers to the finals of the Guinness Premiership and Heineken Cup?

Chapter 33 – Local, Not-Local?

631. Dean Richards

632. Richard Cockerill

633. Dusty Hare

634. Louis Deacon

635. Peter Wheeler

636. Ollie Smith

637. Wavell Wakefield

638. Paul Dodge

639. Neil Back

640. Martin Corry

641. Marcus Rose

642. Steve Johnson

643. Steve Redfern

644. John Wells

645. John Allen

Chapter 34 – Leicester Legends

646. Who was appointed Chairman of the Leicester Tigers in 1996?

647. What was Dean Richard's profession before turning English rugby union professional?

648. How many tries for England did Rory Underwood score?

649. Name the Tiger who scored a try for England against Scotland in the 2013 Six Nations.

650. Can you name the Fijian rugby footballer who scored a try on his Tigers debut against London Welsh in the 2012–13 English Premiership?

651. Can you name Leicester's head coach since July 2010 who left the club at the end of the 2012–13 season to join Leinster?

652. Who made his Tigers début aged 17 in 1996 displacing an ageing England international Rory Underwood from the side?

653. In March 2008, who became the all-time leading points scorer in the Guinness Premiership, overtaking Jonny Wilkinson?

654. Who was popularly known as "The Flying Prince", "The Flying Slav", or simply as "Obo" by many sports fans?

655. After leaving Leicester in 2003, who moved to second division Nuneaton as player-coach?

656. Which Tiger won the Aviva Try of the Season award for 2012–13?

657. Who was dropped from the England side after criticizing Woodward in his book?

658. Name the former Tigers coach inducted into the IRB Hall of Fame in 2011.

659. In 2005 who was appointed Performance Director at Southampton Football Club?

660. Why was Dean Richards banned from rugby for three years?

661. Named in the Sky Sports Dream Team at the Premiership awards in 2008–09, who ended that season with appearances in both Tests against England?

662. Which Tigers legend played in the '98 and '99 Five Nations and the '99 World Cup, missing out on only two possible selections for England's 22 during his test career?

663. Which Leicester legend joined the Barbarians on their Summer 2001 tour of the UK, and then captained the side that came to Welford Road for the Neil Back Testimonial game in March 2003?

664. Who scored 18 tries for Leicester during the 32 games he played in the 2007–08 season?

665. Which Tiger made his debut as a replacement in opening game of 2010 RBS Six Nations?

666. Who partnered his brother Louis in the second row on his Tigers debut in 2003?

667. Whose debut season in 2010–11 ended with an appearance in the Aviva Premiership Final, and selection as Rugby Players Association Player of the Year, and Tigers Supporters' Player of the Year and Newcomer of the Year?

668. Name the Man of the Match and Tigers try-scorer in the 2009–10 Guinness Premiership Final win over London Irish.

669. On his second appearance for the Leicester Tigers senior side, who recorded the fastest hat-trick of tries in Premiership history, doing so in a 13-minute span against Worcester?

670. Name the ball carrying No.8 who made his 100th Tigers start in the Heineken Cup win at the Scarlets in January 2011 and scoring a hat-trick of tries in the win over Treviso a week later.

Chapter 35 – 2010 – Onwards

671. Who made his big breakthrough in the 2009–10 season, scoring 17 points in the historic win over South Africa at Welford Road, and then being named Tigers Players' Player of the Year, Supporters' Young Player of the Year and Rugby Players Association Young Player before scoring a try in the Guinness Premiership Final win over Saracens?

672. Who made his Tigers debut, and entered the record books, in the LV= Cup tie at Leeds aged just 16 years and 237 days in November 2009?

673. Name Tigers Players' Young Player of the Season 2009–10 who became a permanent fixture in the England front row, becoming an ever-present in the Six Nations tournaments of 2010, 2011 and 2012.

674. Who left Leicester for Stade Français, where his 2009–10 Top 14 season was ended early by a 24-week ban for contact with the eye or eye area of Stephen Ferris during Stade's loss to Ulster in the 2009–10 Heineken Cup?

675. Who did the supporters name Newcomer of the Year in 2009–10?

676. Who made his first big impact on the club stage with a try and 13 points in the Tiger's home draw against Ospreys in 2009–10 Heineken Cup when injuries forced Tigers into major changes just ahead of kick-off?

677. Which centre was named Tigers Players' Player of the Year in 2010–11 and picked up the Supporters' Try of the Year award for a solo effort at Bath which began in his own half of the field?

678. Playing at fly-half or centre, who topped 100 points for Leicester Tigers for the first time in 2010–11, scoring 144 points?

679. Who was Named Tigers Young Player of the Year by supporters and team mates after scoring eight tries in his first season of senior rugby in 2010–11?

680. Who in his debut season in 2010–11 for the Tigers ended with an appearance in the Aviva Premiership Final, and selection as Rugby Players Association Player of the Year, and Tigers Supporters' Player of the Year and Newcomer of the Year?

681. Can you name the former Wolverhampton Wanderers footballer who joined the Tigers from Worcester warriors in 2011?

682. Which Tiger collected more than 60% of the votes in picking up the Rugby Players Association Young Player of the Year award in 2011?

683. Who ended 2011–12 with a try for Tigers in the Aviva Premiership Final against Harlequins and then played both midweek games for England against South African Barbarians before returning to Leicester?

684. Which Tiger made his Test debut for Fiji in 2008, scored a match-winning try against Samoa in the 2009 IRB Pacific Nations Cup and a solo try against the All Blacks in 2011?

685. A summer signing in 2011, which young Irishman scored two tries on his Tigers debut against Exeter on the opening day of the season and then added a first European try in the Heineken Cup win over Aironi in Monza?

686. Which international lock scored tries in the final of both Aviva Premiership and LV= Cup in 2011–12, in which he was also named man of the match?

687. In 2011–12 who clocked up his 200th start in Tigers colours and became the first man to reach 250 Premiership appearances?

688. Name the scorer of the decisive second try in the LV= Cup Final win over Northampton Saints in 2012.

689. Name the Tigers prop who captained Italy for the first time in the summer of 2012, leading the team to tour wins over Canada and the USA.

690. Who was the most-capped player in England's Elite Squad for 2012–-13, the fly-half earned his 50th Test cap in the third Test against South Africa in the summer of 2012?

691. Who in 2012 became the first man to make 250 Premiership appearances?

692. Which former Tigers fly-half returned to Welford Road in April 2012 for the match against Leicester but was sent off in the first half by referee Wayne Barnes after hitting his old team mate Tom Croft high and late with his arm?

693. In February 2012 who became the 35th player in the club's history to reach 300 games in the win over Newcastle Falcons?

694. Who picked up a Pacific Nations Cup winners' medal in 2012 with Samoa after playing in wins over Tonga, Fiji and Japan?

695. Which former Tiger was Argentina's Director off Rugby in 2013?

Chapter 36 – Odds and Sods

696. Which former Tiger was appointed Nottingham's Director of Rugby in 1990?

697. Who in 2008 took part in *Strictly Come Dancing* (Series 6)?

698. Which French club did Dean Richards play for prior to returning to England to play for Leicester Tigers?

699. Name the former Tigers and England captain who was appointed head coach at Rugby Lions in National League 3 Midlands League.

700. Which famously competitive and outspoken character had the nickname "The Leicester Lip"?

701. Who played in goal for Notts County and made over 150 appearances as second row forward for the Tigers between 1968 and 1975?

702. Who was the first person to have held every senior post at Leicester Football Club: secretary, captain and president?

703. Which American football club does Martin Johnson support?

704. Dusty Hare played first class cricket for which county?

705. Which former forward was appointed the first President of the Tigers Supporters club?

706. Can you name the brothers, both England internationals who played together for Leicester in the 1933 game against the Barbarians?

707. Martin Johnson was second in the 2004 BBC Sports Personality of the Year award. Who won the Award?

708. The Tigers first game under floodlights, was a 9–19 defeat in February 1960 away at which Welsh club?

709. Tigers' first TV appearance, a 14–0 win against London Scottish on the Richmond Athletic Ground, took place in what year?

710. Tigers' first game on a Sunday on 18 November 1956 was 3–23 loss against which club in Dublin?

711. Which former Tiger was a Battle of Britain pilot who made history in 1942 by becoming the first RAF pilot to be promoted to the rank of air commodore?

712. Can you name the Leicester legend who is thought to have invented the position of 'gully'?

713. Name the brothers who played for the Tigers in the 1983 John Player Cup Final for the Tigers.

714. Whose run of 109 successive first team appearances for the Tigers came to an end against Blackheath in December 1963?

715. Which Leicester legend was voted Whitbread's Rugby World Player of the Year in 1990–91?

716. Who coached the Blue Bulls to four Currie Cup titles in between 2002 and 2006 prior to becoming the Tigers coach?

717. How many full international rugby union games has Welford Road staged – 7, 9 or 11? 7

718.   Named in the Sky Sports Dream Team at the Premiership awards in 2008–09, who ended that season with appearances in both Tests against England?

719.   Who partnered his brother Louis in the second row on his Tigers debut in 2003?

720.   Which lock who joined Tigers during the summer from Irish province Leinster made his international debut for Ireland against the All Blacks in Auckland in June 2002, and toured with Ireland to Japan in June playing in both tests?

Chapter 37 – Premiership Finals

721. What is the venue for the Premiership Final?

722. In what year was the first Premiership Final held?

723. Which two teams contested the first Premiership Final?

724. Which team won the inaugural Premiership Final?

725. Which team has won the Premiership Final on the most occasions?

726. Between 2001 and 2012 how many times have Leicester Tigers reached the Premiership Final?

727. How many times did the Leicester Tigers finish top of the league between 2001 and 2012? 6

728. Have the Tigers won the Premiership Crown without finishing top of the League?

729. Can you name both Tigers try scores in the 45–20 defeat by Sale Sharks in the 2006 Premiership Final?

730. Who was man of the match as Tigers beat Gloucester 44–16 in the Premiership Final in 2007 at Twickenham to win their first league title since 2002?

731. Who coached the Tigers to Premiership title success in 2007?

732. London Wasps beat Leicester in the 2008 Premiership Final in front of over 80,000 spectators at Twickenham. What was the final score?

733. Leicester won the 2009 Premiership Final. Who did they beat 10-9?

734. Name the Man of the Match and try-scorer in the 2009 Premiership Final win over London Irish.

735. The Tigers retained the Premiership title in 2010 – the club's third in four years and ninth in total. Who did Leicester beat 33–27 in a thrilling Twickenham final?

736. Who scored a try for Leicester on the 13th minute for the Tigers in the 2010 Premiership final?

737. The Tigers win at Twickenham in 2010 was sealed with a late try from who?

738. Leicester reached the Premiership final in 2011. Who were Leicester's opponents?

739. Who scored the only try in the 2011 Premiership Final?

740. Who scored all of the Tigers points in the 2011 Premiership Final?

741. What was the final score in the 2011 Premiership Final?

742. Which did the Tigers beat to reach the 2012 Premiership Final?

743. Who scored 13 points for the Tigers in the 2012 Premiership Final?

744. Which team won the 2012 Premiership Final?

745. Who did Leicester beat to secure a place in the 2013 Premiership Final?

746. Which team finished top of the Premier League in 2013 but failed to reach the Premiership Final?

747. Leicester secured their 10th English title with a 37–17 win against Northampton in 2013. Can you Leicester's four try scorers?

748. The Tigers and England fly-half had to come off with concussion towards the end of the first half of the 2013 Premiership Final following a late tackle by which Saint?

749. Name Northampton's captain who in 2013 became the first player to be sent off in a Premiership Final.

750. Who was voted Man of the Match in the 2013 Premiership Final?

Answers

1 Answers – In the Beginning...

1. August 1880
2. George Hotel, Leicester
3. Leicester Societies AFC, Leicester Amateur FC and Leicester Alert
4. Black
5. Moseley
6. Belgrave Cricket and Cycle Ground
7. True
8. 2d
9. 3
10. True
11. Ended 0–0
12. Midland Counties Cup – beat Moseley 5–3 in April 1898
13. Arthur Jones
14. Victoria Park
15. Moseley
16. 1891
17. 1892
18. Leicestershire Rugby Union
19. Bedford
20. Blackheath
21. W. R. Hesmondhalgh
22. 10,000
23. To give other sides a chance to win the Cup
24. 71–0
25. True
26. 20 shillings
27. Tom Crumbie
28. Sid Penny
29. Bedford Grammar School
30. Arthur Jones

2 Answers – Older or Younger?

31. Same age (1880)
32. Older (1865)
33. Older (1877)
34. Younger (1888)
35. Older (1866)
36. Younger (1885)
37. Older (1861)
38. Older (1871)
39. Older (1873)
40. Older (1877)

3 Answers – RFU Club Competition

41. 1972
42. Gloucester
43. Bath (10)
44. Gloucester
45. Leicester 15–12 Moseley
46. London Irish and Gosforth
47. 3 (1983, 1989 and 1993)
48. Pilkington
49. True
50. Bath

4 Answers – Edwardian Tigers

51. Kingsholm, Gloucester
52. 1902
53. 14000
54. Jack Miles
55. All Blacks
56. 70%

57. True
58. Alfred Hind
59. Oxford
60. Professionalism
61. John Jackett, Tom Smith, Fred Jackson
62. Gil Hopkins
63. 1909
64. False, 9–9 draw
65. Harry Lawrie
66. Newbold-upon-Avon
67. Belgrave Premier Works
68. Percy Lawrie
69. Barbarians
70. True

5 Answers – Heineken Cup

71. 1995–96
72. Due to restrictions on alcohol sponsorship
73. England, France, Ireland, Italy, Scotland, Wales
74. 24 (6 pools of 4 teams)
75. Toulouse
76. European Challenge Cup
77. Toulouse
78. Bath in 1998
79. Leicester Tigers
80. Cardiff

6 Answers – 1997 Heineken Cup Final

81. 20
82. 0
83. Toulouse
84. Cardiff Arms Park

85.   France

86.   Brive 8–6 Leicester

87.   John Liley

88.   Yes – in the 54th minute

89.   100 metres

90.   Christophe Lamaison

7 Answers – Captain Fantastic

91.   John Allen

92.   Tom Berry

93.   Jack Sturges

94.   Graham Willars

95.   Peter Wheeler

96.   Ian Smith

97.   Paul Dodge

98.   Bernard Gadney

99.   Frank Prentice

100.   Harry Greenlees

101.   Billy Foreman

102.   Paul Dodge

103.   Kevin Andrews

104.   Bobby Barr

105.   Martin Corry

106.   4

107.   Martin Corry

108.   Harold Day

109.   Geordan Murphy

110.   Bob Rowell

8 Answers – 1920s Tigers

111.   Harold Day
112.   Ernest Prescott.
113.   Edward Haselmere
114.   Racing Club de France.
115.   France
116.   Alistair Smallwood
117.   True
118.   Wavell Wakefield
119.   All Blacks
120.   £1,000
121.   True
122.   Harold Day
123.   Eclipse
124.   Percy Lawrie
125.   1926
126.   A C Tole
127.   Harold Day
128.   Cardiff
129.   Eric Thorneloe
130.   Richmond

9 Answers – Premiership Tigers Records

131.   Geordan Murphy
132.   Tim Stimpson
133.   59
134.   Newcastle Falcons
135.   45–10 defeat by Wasps in 1998
136.   17
137.   False they lost five
138.   Merlin Davies 37 years 300 days
139.   12 against West Hartlepool in 1999
140.   Neil Back

10 Answers – 2001 Heineken Cup Final

141. 1 (Pontypridd)
142. Pau
143. Leicester 41–10 Swansea
144. Gloucester
145. Watford's Vicarage Road
146. Stade Français
147. Martin Johnson
148. Pat Howard
149. 44,000
150. Tim Stimpson
151. Jamie Hamilton
152. Diego Domínguez
153. Leon Lloyd
154. Neil Back
155. Leicester 34–30 Stade Francais

11 Answers – 1930s Tigers

156. Doug Prentice
157. Waterloo
158. Bath
159. 7
160. George Beamish
161. Charles Slow
162. 25,000
163. Leicestershire & East Midlands 30–21 Springboks
164. Tom Berry
165. Bernard Gadney
166. Graham Meikle
167. Matchday programmes
168. 3d
169. Robert Barr

170. 1934
171. Alexander Obolensky
172. Fred Doe
173. S.F. Herbert
174. Coventry
175. Blackheath

12 Answers – International Tigers

176. Rory Underwood
177. Brian Smith
178. Ken Scotland
179. Dean Richards
180. 7
181. Dusty Hare, Paul Dodge, Clive Walker and Peter Wheeler
182. George Beamish
183. John Elliott
184. Toby Flood
185. Ben Kay
186. Paul Dodge
187. France
188. Brian Ashton
189. Toby Flood
190. Tom Varndell
191. Rory Underwood
192. Will Greenwood
193. Neil Back
194. Martin Corry
195. Heyneke Meyer
196. Jordan Crane
197. 27
198. Dan Cole
199. Richard Cockerill
200. 8

13 Answers – Anglo Welsh Cup

201. 4
202. London Wasps
203. Llanelli Scarlets
204. 3 (2007, 2008 and 2012)
205. 2 (2007 and 2012)
206. Newport Gwent Dragons
207. Sale Sharks
208. Cardiff
209. Tom Varndell
210. George Ford
211. Sixways Stadium, Worcester
212. Northampton
213. Stephen Myler
214. Steve Mafi and Scott Hamilton
215. Llanelli Scarlets and Saracens

14 Answers – 1940s Tigers

216. Leicester Harlequins
217. Tom Berry
218. Cardiff
219. 20 games for the senior side which earned the players a tie
220. Melville Channer
221. Hadyn Thomas
222. Cardiff
223. Harlequins
224. Harold Jerwood
225. Ernie Watkin (224 points)

15 Answers – World Cup Tigers

226. 1987
227. Dean Richards
228. Martin Johnson
229. Martin Johnson, Will Greenwood, Neil Back
230. Lewis Moody
231. Will Greenood
232. Marcos Ayerza
233. Ben Kay
234. Ben Kay
235. Martin Corry
236. Toby Flood
237. Will Greenwood
238. Marcelo Loffreda
239. Joel Stransky
240. John Wells

16 Answers – Heineken Cup Winners

241. Toulouse
242. Bath
243. Ulster
244. Northampton Saints
245. Toulouse
246. London Wasps
247. Toulouse
248. Munster
249. Leinster
250. Leinster

17 Answers – 1950s Tigers

251. George Cullen
252. Bob Weighill
253. Gwynne Lawrence and Bill Moore
254. Bill Moore
255. 1951
256. Robert Stirling
257. Moseley
258. Ken Jones
259. £250
260. Swansea
261. The 'A' team
262. David Matthews
263. George Cullen
264. Old Belvedere
265. Eric Thorneloe
266. Ian Swan
267. John Elders
268. Tony O'Reilly
269. John Thompson
270. Michael Gavins

18 Answers – What Year – Rugby Union

271. 1871
272. 2000
273. 1995
274. 1987
275. 1900
276. 1843
277. 1871
278. 1992
279. 1970
280. 1909

19 Answers- 1960s Tigers

281. David Matthews
282. David Matthews
283. Keith Chilton
284. Newport
285. Colin Martin
286. Bedford
287. Tom Bleasdale
288. 15
289. David Mathews
290. 1964
291. Big freeze
292. 300
293. Tiger skin
294. Dead rat
295. John Quick
296. Danny Hearn
297. Chalkie White
298. Mike Jones
299. David Matthews
300. Peter Wheeler

20 Answers – Welford Road

301. True
302. 4th Leicestershire Regiment
303. Transvaal
304. Sid Penny
305. 6
306. Stoneygate
307. 19,800
308. True
309. 24,000

310. Italy
311. Newcastle Falcons
312. South Africa
313. 10,000
314. Holland & Barrett Stand
315. De Montfort and Leicester
316. Percy Lawrie
317. 17,000
318. Dusty Hare
319. 11
320. James Morrison

21 Answers – 1970s Tiger

321. John Duggan
322. Bleddyn Jones
323. Bob Barker
324. Peter Wheeler
325. 600
326. True
327. Dusty Hare
328. Eric Bann
329. Nottingham
330. Bob Barker
331. No: 998 points and 29 wins
332. John Ingleby
333. Bob Barker
334. David Matthews
335. Robin Cowling
336. Bleddyn Jones and Frank Jones
337. Les Cusworth
338. Paul Dodge
339. Eric Bann
340. William 'Dusty' Hare

341. Mountain Ash

342. Peter Wheeler

343. Bob Barker

344. Hartlepool Rovers

345. William Henry

346. True

347. Brian Hall

348. Northampton

349. Coventry

350. Gloucester

351. Leicester 3–6 Gloucester

352. Dusty Hare

353. 24,000

354. Paul Dodge

355. Bleddyn Jones

356. Peter Wheeler

357. 2,000

358. Les Cusworth

359. Dusty Hare

360. Bedford

361. 43–7

362. Mick Newton and Tim Barnwell

363. Gosport

364. Peter Wheeler

365. 18,000

366. Dusty Hare

367. Rob Laird for Moseley

368. Moseley 9–3 Leicester

369. Steve Kenney

370. John Duggan

22 Answers – 2002 Heineken Cup Final

371. Leicester 15–9 Munster
372. Martin Johnson
373. Mick Galway
374. Cardiff Millennium Stadium
375. Freddie Tuilagi
376. Martin Johnson
377. Geordan Murphy
378. Ronan O'Gara
379. Tim Stimpson
380. Austin Healey

23 Answers – British Lion Tigers

381. 1888
382. 1930
383. John Robins
384. Fran Cotton
385. Dusty Hare
386. Neil Back
387. Austin Healey, Martin Johnson, Neil Back, Martin Corry and Dorian West (replacement),
388. Peter Wheeler
389. Martin Johnson
390. Tom Croft
391. Tom Croft
392. 6
393. Bernard Gadney
394. Martin Corry
395. Dan Cole, Tom Croft, Geoff Parling, Manusamoa Tuilagi, Ben Youngs and Tom Youngs

24 Answers – 1980s Tigers

396.   Barry Evans

397.   Les Cusworth

398.   Dusty Hare

399.   Peter Wheeler

400.   Northampton

401.   Orrell

402.   Peter Wheeler, Dusty Hare, Paul Dodge, Clive Woodward

403.   Moseley

404.   Dusty Hare

405.   Les Cusworth

406.   Harlequins

407.   London Irish

408.   Leicester 21–9 London Irish

409.   Les Cusworth

410.   Dusty Hare (319) and Les Cusworth (173)

411.   Peter Wheeler and Clive Woodward

412.   Paul Dodge

413.   True

414.   London Welsh

415.   12–12

416.   Les Cusworth

417.   Gosforth

418.   Peter Wheeler

419.   15,000

420.   Steve Kenney Tim Barnwell, Dusty Hare

421.   True

422.   De Montfort Hall

423.   £4

424.   Leicester 15–18 Australia

425.   Moseley

426.   Dean Richards

427.   Barry Evans

428. Nick Jackson
429. Bristol
430. Steve Johnson
431. Tim Barnwell
432. Barry Evans
433. 57
434. Rory Underwood
435. For not opposing RFU's tour of South Africa
436. Dusty Hare
437. 7
438. Ind Coope
439. Steve Redfern
440. Rory Underwood
441. Dusty Hare
442. Bath
443. Dusty Hare
444. 9
445. Les Cusworth
446. Gosforth
447. Rory Underwood and Dean Richards
448. Les Cusworth
449. Martin Johnson
450. Les Cusworth
451. 58,000
452. Bath 10–6 Leicester
453. Dusty Hare
454. True
455. Ian Smith

25 Answers – Home Grounds

456. Bath
457. Saracens
458. Northampton
459. London Welsh
460. Exeter Chiefs
461. London Wasps
462. Worcester Warriors
463. Gloucester
464. Harlequins
465. London Irish

26 Answers – Author Author!

466. Dean Richards
467. Clive Woodward
468. Rory Underwood
469. Neil Back
470. Geordan Murphy
471. Lewis Moody
472. Peter Wheeler
473. Austin Healey
474. Richard Cockerill
475. Will Greenwood

27 Answers – Left Leicester

476. London Irish
477. Nottingham
478. Cambridge University
479. Wasps
480. Harlequin
481. Bath

482. Gloucester
483. Bath
484. Bath
485. London Wasps
486. Leinster
487. Gloucester
488. London Irish
489. Melrose
490. Gloucester
491. Montpellier Hérault Rugby
492. Bedford Blues
493. London Irish
494. Bath
495. Newcastle Falcons

28 Answers – 1990s

496. Twice (1995 and 1999)
497. 0
498. Twice (1993 and 1997)
499. Steve Hackney
500. Darren Garforth
501. John Liley
502. Dean Richards
503. Les Cusworth
504. Rory Underwood
505. Steve Kenney
506. Barry Evans
507. 6th
508. Swifts
509. Tony Russ
510. £20,000
511. Les Cusworth
512. John Liley

513. Coventry
514. Bath 0–12 Leicester
515. Roslyn Park
516. Rob Andrews
517. Dean Richards
518. Leicester 100–0 Liverpool St Helens
519. Tony Underwood
520. Richard Cockerill
521. 5
522. Exeter
523. Tony Underwood
524. Northampton
525. Leicester 8–6 Wasps
526. Wasps
527. Peter Winterbottom
528. Brian Moore
529. Graham Rowntree, Richard Cockerill and Darren Garforth
530. 4 to 1
531. Martin Johnson
532. Leicester 23–16 Harlequins
533. 13,000
534. Bob Dwyer
535. Neil Back
536. Lewis Moody
537. Allied Dunbar
538. Will Greenwood
539. In the Pilkington Cup final defeat against Bath. As the final whistle was blown, Back pushed referee Steve Lander to the ground. Back maintained that he had mistaken Lander for Bath back-row (and future England head coach) Andy Robinson.
540. 6
541. Wasps
542. Glasgow
543. Joel Strantsky
544. Dean Richards
545. Newcastle Falcons

29 Answers – Join Leicester

546.	Gloucester
547.	Moseley
548.	Richmond
549.	Nottingham
550.	Nottingham
551.	Orrell
552.	Newcaste Falcons
553.	San Donà
554.	Gloucester
555.	Pontypool RFC
556.	Parma
557.	Bristol
558.	Biarritz
559.	Bristol
560.	Bedford Blues
561.	Gloucester
562.	Saracens
563.	Brive
564.	Rotherham
565.	Stade Francais

30 Answers – What Year – Tigers

566.	1964
567.	1999
568.	1885
569.	2001
570.	1997
571.	1926
572.	1990
573.	1891
574.	1993

575. 2012
576. 1891
577. 1909
578. 2009
579. 1980
580. 2012

31 Answers 1987– 88 Courage League

581. 12
582. True
583. 4
584. 1
585. Bath
586. Waterlooville
587. 10
588. Moseley
589. Les Cusworth away at Nottingham in November 1987
590. Sale
591. Orrell
592. Wasps
593. Gloucester
594. Nottingham
595. Sale

32 Answers – Tigers – 2000s

596. 5 (2000, 2001, 2002, 2007 and 2009)
597. Twice (2001 & 2002)
598. Once (2007)
599. Austin Healey.
600. 4
601. 5
602. Saracens

603. Sale
604. Will Greenwood
605. Saracens
606. Newcastle Falcons
607. Bath
608. True
609. Gloucester
610. Neil Back
611. Andy Goode
612. Ben Kay
613. French champions Biarritz
614. 2
615. Josh Kronfeld
616. Newcastle.
617. 57
618. Neil Back
619. 7
620. Saracens
621. Tom Varndell
622. Dean Richards
623. Pat Howard
624. Louis Deacon
625. Ben Youngs
626. Marcelo Loffreda
627. Toby Flood
628. Heyneke Meyer
629. Lucas Amorosino scored the only try with Ben Youngs kicking the rest of the points.
630. Richard Cockerill

33 Answers – Local, Not Local

631. Not Local
632. Not Local
633. Not Local
634. Local
635. Not Local
636. Local
637. Not Local
638. Local
639. Not Local
640. Not Local
641. Local
642. Not Local
643. Local
644. Not Local
645. Not Local

34 Answers – Leicester legend

646. Peter Tom CBE
647. Police Constable
648. 49
649. Geoff Parling
650. Vereniki Goneve
651. Matt O'Connor
652. Leon Lloyd
653. Andy Goode
654. Alexander Obolensky
655. Darren Garforth
656. Dan Bowden (Leicester Tigers v Saracens – 23 February 2013)
657. Richard Cockerill
658. Bob Dwyer
659. Clive Woodward

660. Bloodgate – he had orchestrated and had "central control" over a fake blood injury to Harlequins player Tom Williams during a Heineken Cup fixture against Leinster.
661. Marcos Ayerza
662. Richard Cockerill
663. Richard Cockerill
664. Tom Varndell
665. Dan Cole
666. Brett Deacon
667. Thomas Waldrom
668. Jordan Crane
669. Tom Varndell
670. Jordan Crane

35 Answers 2010 - Onwards

671. Ben Youngs
672. George Ford
673. Dan Cole
674. Julien Dupuy
675. Geoff Parling
676. Billy Twelvetrees
677. Anthony Allen
678. Billy Twelvetress
679. Manusamoa Tuilagi
680. Thomas Waldrom
681. Graham Kitchener
682. Manusamoa Tuilagi
683. Anthony Allen
684. Vereniki Goneva
685. Niall Morris
686. Steve Mafi
687. George Chuter
688. Scott Hamilton

689. Martin Castrogiovanni
690. Toby Flood
691. George Chuter
692. Andy Goode
693. Geordan Murphy
694. Logovi'l Mulipola
695. Les Cusworth

36 Answers – Odds and Sods

696. Dusty Hare
697. Austin Healey
698. Roanne
699. Neil Back
700. Austin Healey
701. Eric Barr
702. John Parsons
703. San Francisco 49ers
704. Nottinghamshire
705. Charlie Cross
706. Graham and Stephen Meikle
707. Jonny Wilkinson
708. Newport
709. 1951
710. Old Belvedere
711. George Beamish
712. Arthur Jones
713. Stuart and Steve Redfern
714. David Mathews
715. Dean Richards
716. Heyneke Meyer
717. 7
718. Marcos Ayerza
719. Brett Deacon
720. Leo Cullen

37 Answers – Premiership Finals

721.   Twickenham
722.   2001
723.   Leicester Tigers and Bath
724.   Leicester Tigers
725.   Leicester Tigers and Wasps – 4 times each
726.   9
727.   6
728.   Yes in 2007
729.   Jim Hamilton and Lewis Moody
730.   Alesana Tuilagi
731.   Pat Howard
732.   Wasps 26–16 Leicester
733.   London Irish
734.   Jordan Crane
735.   Saracens
736.   Matt Smith
737.   Dan Hipkiss
738.   Saracens
739.   James Sure
740.   Toby Flood
741.   Leicester 18–22 Saracens
742.   Northampton
743.   George Ford
744.   Harlequins
745.   Harlequins
746.   Saracens
747.   Niall Morris, Graham Kitchener, Manusamoa Tuilagi, Vereniki
        Goneva
748.   Courtney Lawes
749.   Dylan Hartley
750.   Anthony Allen

.

NIGEL FREESTONE

7886306R00068

Printed in Great Britain
by Amazon.co.uk, Ltd.,
Marston Gate.